90-Minute Shakespeare:
ROMEO AND JULIET

By William Shakespeare
Adapted by Diane Timmerman

YOUNG ACTORS SERIES

A SMITH AND KRAUS BOOK

For Steve, Charis, and Barek

And for my students and colleagues
at Butler University

A Smith and Kraus Book
Published by Smith and Kraus, Inc.
177 Lyme Road, Hanover, NH 03755

First Edition: July 2001
10 9 8 7 6 5 4 3 2 1

Cover and Text Design
by Julia Hill Gignoux, Freedom Hill Design
Cover Art: Production Design and Photography
by Madeleine Sobota
Alecia White as Juliet and Jacob Saylor as Romeo
Author Photo by Ed Moss

The Library of Congress Cataloging-In-Publication Data
Timmerman, Diane.
90-Minute Shakespeare / by William Shakespeare ; adapted by Diane Timmerman.
—1st ed.
p. cm. — (Young actors series)
Contents: [v.1]. Romeo and Juliet — [v.2]. A midsummer night's dream
Summary: Presents scripts for two of William Shakespeare's classic plays,
edited so that they can be performed in ninety minutes.

ISBN 1-57525-238-4 Romeo and Juliet
ISBN 1-57525-290-2 A Midsummer Night's Dream

1. Shakespeare, William, 1564–1616—Adaptations—Juvenile literature.
[1. Shakespeare, William, 1564–1616—Plays.] I. Title: Ninety-minute Shakespeare.
II. Shakespeare, William 1564–1616. III. Title. IV. Young actors series.
PR2877 .T5 2001
822.3'3—dc21
2001034392

Introduction

Romeo and Juliet is one of world's greatest love stories, a sweeping tale of passion, prejudice, and poetry. Why would anyone want to cut this majestic play to ninety minutes? For me, the reasons for adapting and directing a ninety-minute *Romeo and Juliet* are compelling. I love Shakespeare's images, characters, and stories. I marvel at the immediacy of the language 400 years after the words were penned. I despair when I sit through painstaking productions that alienate audiences because of their length. Strong evidence suggests that the original running times of Shakespeare's plays were much briefer than our current productions. One need look no further than the Prologue of *Romeo and Juliet* to note that Elizabethans must have spoken the poetry at a quick pace. The Prologue tells us that the star-crossed lovers' story will be "the two hours traffic of our stage." Most contemporary uncut productions of *Romeo and Juliet* run at least three hours. By contrast, the Elizabethan productions zipped by at a lively, entertaining pace, their ears hearing with the same dexterous speed as our modern day eyes see. I wanted to capture that zestful spirit for contemporary audiences. And so, without altering Shakespeare's words, I edited this great play (and four others in this series) to its essential core. Shakespeare's characters still speak their lines in magnificent iambic pentameter and prose; they just speak fewer of them. Is this kosher? What would Bill think? Is it wrong to shorten these sacred, canonical plays? I actually think it is okay. And I think Bill would agree. Since talking and listening at the Elizabethan rate is not possible for us, surely he wouldn't mind if we occasionally shortened his scripts. Bill valued entertaining his audiences and just might approve of a running time that leaves audiences wanting to see another Shakespeare production—maybe even a full-length one. He'd undoubtedly prefer that reaction to exhausted audiences exiting the theater vowing never to return again.

Who might use this *Romeo and Juliet* script? Equity theaters operating under the ninety-minute Theater for Young Audiences contract, colleges, high schools, middle schools and community theaters—any group desiring a shorter running time to satisfy their own needs or those of their audience. For me, this adaptation saw its first life as a production of the Butler Essential Shakespeare Series at Butler University in Indianapolis. Wanting to provide our Department of Theater students with an annual opportunity to perform Shakespeare and desiring to create an educational outreach program to area middle and high school students, the Butler Essential Shakespeare Series was born. Each year, I adapted and directed one of the plays in this series. During the rehearsal period, cast and crew members would travel with me to area schools where we would do fencing demonstrations, scenes from the play, and Shakespearean acting workshops. The highlight of these visits was the informal conversation between the college students and the not-too-much-younger middle and high school students. How do you understand what the language means, the younger students wanted to know. With pride the college students would explain their process—how they studied the text, made the words their own, and ultimately reveled in the sheer thrill of playing Shakespeare. These conversations, along with the raucous laughter and rapt attention during the student matinees, proved what everyone in education knows: The message is most powerful when it comes not from on high, but from a near peer. Witnessing students only a few years older than them succeed in bold, visceral Shakespearean performances left indelible delight in our young audiences. The weeks of losing the battle to understand the bard (despite help from twenty-year-old videos) melted away when these students saw that Shakespeare was comprehensible, relevant, and fun! That the student matinees were successful was not a surprise—that the general public embraced the ninety-minute format was. Our evening performances became campus and citywide events. The shorter time frame worked wonders for jaded adults who had sworn off Shakespeare. Elated at the end of the comedies, moved at the end of the tragedies, these grown-ups left the theater happy to have been there. The most uttered comment I heard was: "What was cut? It seemed like that was the whole play." Perhaps the pendulum will swing back in this sound-bite age of ours. We can always hope that channel surfing will be reduced and attention spans will lengthen. Until then, my text-lover status notwithstanding, I choose to bring people back to the theater to love Shakespeare—if only so they will once again find the courage to see a full-length production.

How did I edit this script? Let me count the ways. Mostly by trimming each existing scene. In a few cases, by eliminating small scenes and characters altogether. Functioning as part-director, part-iambic pentameter police, my editing goal was to create a playable script that respected the verse, the characters, and the story. Conceptual ideas of how I might direct *Romeo and Juliet* no doubt influenced the editing choices I made. (And editing the play gave me a headstart on the directing process.) Many cuts were easy to make; other choices were more painful. Although the adaptation was mainly completed before the rehearsal process began, invaluable tweaking took place as the actors played the text on their feet. Only then did some redundancies and leaps in logic emerge. Spirited debate over the intricacies of the text reigned during rehearsal, with actors comparing their shortened scenes to the full-length versions, filling up their performances with the power of the full text. For this adaptation, I was able to retain all major characters and plotlines. I did give the Chorus's lines to the Prince (a practice of many full-length productions), conflated Abram and Balthasar into one character, and cut Friar John and Paris's Page altogether. For the trickier maneuvers, I confess to altering a word here or there to make the action coherent. Otherwise, the words are Shakespeare's.

How to produce this play? Many groups using this script already have a clear idea of their production goals. I offer a few tips here that might prove helpful for some. This adaptation is intentionally devoid of the translation notes found in most Shakespeare editions, enabling the book to function as a script. It is understood that the director, designers, and cast members will use full-length editions of *Romeo and Juliet* for clarification of individual words as well as larger plot and action questions. If a transition appears awkward in the adaptation, revisit the full-length script, where you will usually find that the transition can be accomplished through physical action on the stage. Indeed, the success of a ninety-minute Shakespeare production lies in the physicality of the staging. Because much of the language has been cut, the story must be told in stage pictures and through physical movement—even more than one might employ in full-length productions. And because movement adds time, your first read-through may finish in only fifty minutes. During the course of the rehearsal period, when physical action, sound cues, music, dances, and swordfights are added, the running time will sneak back up to ninety minutes. All of these elements will enhance the production, adding structure and helping to tell the story. For *Romeo and Juliet*, four main junctures where music can successfully meld with movement are the opening fight sequence, the Capulet dance, the Tybalt/Mercutio/Romeo fight, and the final scene at the grave. Whether your production utilizes a contemporary or classical sound, stylized or realistic fight choreography, these four events benefit from the support of sound and movement. Brief transitional music makes leaps in location and time clearer as well.

The large cast list for this play includes a few doubling suggestions, although many organizations may need to do additional doubling. Many roles may be played nontraditionally, a practice that works particularly well with Shakespeare. Casting women to play male roles (as men) works especially well for

Tybalt, Mercutio, Balthasar, and other servants. Some male characters may, with a change of pronouns, be switched to female characters: the Apothecary plays well as a woman, as does the Prince. Many of the servants can simply become androgynous. Color-blind casting works well for any role.

Everyone involved in theater knows it is a team sport. This script was successfully adapted and produced because I am lucky to work with wonderful colleagues and amazing students whose talent and enthusiasm made the Butler Essential Shakespeare Series a joyful artistic enterprise. To the entire company of *Romeo and Juliet*, I say "Thank you!"

Artistic projects are born out of an abundance of the soul, an overflowing of love and passion so great one must express it in a way that transcends the everyday language of our lives. Only by being blessed with the love of my best friend and husband, Steve Webb, and the inspiration of our children, Charis and Barek, do I find the courage to work on great Shakespearean texts. Their love and Shakespeare's words make me feel small and humbled—and completely invincible.

Romeo and Juliet was first performed in the Lilly Hall Studio Theatre at Butler University in Indianapolis, Indiana, on October 28, 1999. It was subsequently presented in Clowes Memorial Hall on November 2, 1999. The cast was as follows:

PRINCE OF VERONA	Beth Weaver
MERCUTIO	Tavi Stutz
PARIS	Malaki Kindred
MONTAGUE	Jason Reed
LADY MONTAGUE	Kelly Baas
ROMEO	Jacob Saylor
BENVOLIO	Mike Vanlandingham
BALTHASAR	Kate McCutcheon
CAPULET	Kevin Lind
LADY CAPULET	Michele McCarty
JULIET	Alecia White
TYBALT	Cassie Pappas
JULIET'S NURSE	Katie Kalb
GREGORY/Second Watchman	Mandy Keller
SAMPSON/First Watchman	Sean Hildreth
FRIAR LAURENCE	John Hammerle
APOTHECARY/Capulet's Servant	Liz Jackson
DANCERS/Fighters	Krista Amigone, Cory Gram
	Jason Henschen, Tanner Hronek
	Jessica Johnson, Aaron Selissen
	Jennifer Sutton, Jennifer Sydor

Director	Diane Timmerman
Scenic/Lighting Designer	Madeleine Sobota
Costume Designer	Nicole Sobota
Composer	Frank Felice
Choreographer	Cynthia Pratt
Fight Choreographer	Rob Johansen
Technical Director	Glen Thoreson
Stage Manager	Brandy Rodgers

CAST OF CHARACTERS

Escalus, Prince of Verona
Mercutio, a young gentleman and kinsman to the Prince,
    friend of Romeo
Paris, a noble young kinsman to the Prince
Montague, head of a Veronese family at feud with the
    Capulets
Lady Montague
Romeo, Montague's son
Benvolio, Montague's nephew and friend of Romeo and
    Mercutio
Balthasar, Romeo's servant
Capulet, head of a Veronese family at feud with the
    Montagues
Lady Capulet
Juliet, Capulet's daughter
Tybalt, Lady Capulet's nephew
Nurse, to Juliet
Gregory, servant to Capulet
Sampson, servant to Capulet
Friar Laurence, of the Fransiscan Order
An Apothecary, of Mantua
First Watchman (played by Sampson)
Second Watchman (played by Gregory)
Third Watchman
Citizens of Verona; revelers at the Capulet's

Prologue

PRINCE
>Two households, both alike in dignity,
>From ancient grudge break to new mutiny.
>A pair of star-cross'd lovers take their life;
>Do with their death bury their parents' strife.
>The fearful passage of their death-mark'd love,
>Is now the fateful traffic of our stage;
>The which if you with patient ears attend,
>What here shall miss, our toil shall strive to mend.

Act 1, Scene 1

Verona. A public place.

(Enter SAMPSON and GREGORY, of the house of Capulet, armed with swords and bucklers.)

GREGORY
>The quarrel is between our masters and us their men.

SAMPSON
>'Tis all one.

GREGORY
>Draw thy sword! Here comes one of the house of the Montagues.

SAMPSON
>Quarrel, I will back thee.

GREGORY
>I will frown as he passes by, and let him take it as he lists.

SAMPSON
I will bite my thumb at him;
which is a disgrace to him, if he bears it.

(Enter BALTHASAR.)

BALTHASAR
Do you bite your thumb at me, sir?

SAMPSON
I do bite my thumb, sir.

BALTHASAR
Do you bite your thumb at me, sir?

SAMPSON
(Aside to GREGORY.) Is the law of our side, if I say ay?

GREGORY
No.

SAMPSON
No, sir, I do not bite my thumb at you, sir, but I
bite my thumb, sir.

GREGORY
Do you quarrel, sir?

BALTHASAR
Quarrel sir! No, sir.

SAMPSON
If you do, sir, I am for you: I serve as good a man as you.
Draw, if you be a man.

(They fight.)
(Enter BENVOLIO.)

BENVOLIO
Part, fools!
Put up your swords; you know not what you do.

(Beats down their swords.)

GREGORY
Here comes one of my master's kinsmen.

(Enter TYBALT.)

TYBALT
What, art thou drawn among these heartless hinds?
Turn thee, Benvolio, look upon thy death.

BENVOLIO
I do but keep the peace: put up thy sword,
Or manage it to part these men with me.

TYBALT
What, drawn, and talk of peace! I hate the word,
As I hate hell, all Montagues, and thee:
Have at thee, coward!

(They fight.)
(Enter, several of both houses, who join the fray.)

CITIZENS
Strike! Beat them down!
Down with the Capulets! Down with the Montagues!

(Enter CAPULET and LADY CAPULET.)

CAPULET
    What noise is this? Give me my long sword, ho!

LADY CAPULET
    A crutch, a crutch! Why call you for a sword?

CAPULET
    My sword, I say! Old Montague is come.

(Enter MONTAGUE and LADY MONTAGUE.)

MONTAGUE
    Thou villain Capulet! —Hold me not, let me go.

LADY MONTAGUE
    Thou shalt not stir a foot to seek a foe.

(Enter PRINCE.)

PRINCE
    Rebellious subjects, enemies to peace,
    Throw your mistemper'd weapons to the ground,
    And hear the sentence of your moved prince.
    If ever you disturb our streets again,
    Your lives shall pay the forfeit of the peace.
    For this time, all the rest depart away:
    You Capulet, shall go along with me:
    And, Montague, come you this afternoon,
    To know our further pleasure in this case.
    Once more, on pain of death, all men depart.

*(Exeunt all but MONTAGUE, LADY MONTAGUE, and
BENVOLIO.)*

LADY MONTAGUE
    O, where is Romeo? Saw you him today?
    Right glad I am he was not at this fray.

BENVOLIO
    So early walking did I see your son.

MONTAGUE
    Many a morning hath he walking been,
    With tears augmenting the fresh morning dew.

BENVOLIO
    My noble uncle, do you know the cause?

MONTAGUE
    I neither know it nor can learn of him.
    Could we but learn from whence his sorrows grow,
    We would as willingly give cure as know.

BENVOLIO
    I'll know his grievance, or be much denied.

(Exeunt.)

Act 1, Scene 2

A street.

(Enter CAPULET, PARIS, and Servant.)

CAPULET
    But Montague is bound as well as I,
    In penalty alike; and 'tis not hard, I think,
    For men so old as we to keep the peace.

PARIS
    Of honourable reckoning are you both;
    And pity 'tis you lived at odds so long.
    But now, my lord, what say you to my suit?

CAPULET
    My child is yet a stranger in the world.

PARIS
    Younger than she are happy mothers made.

CAPULET
    And too soon marr'd are those so early made.
    But woo her, gentle Paris, get her heart,
    My will to her consent is but a part.
    This night I hold an old accustom'd feast,
    Whereto I have invited many a guest
    Such as I love; and you, among the store,
    One more, most welcome, makes my number more.
    Come, go with me.

(To Servant, giving a paper.)

    Go, sirrah, trudge about
    Through fair Verona; find those persons out

Whose names are written there, and to them say
My house and welcome on their pleasure stay.

(Exeunt CAPULET and PARIS.)
(Enter BENVOLIO and ROMEO.)

BENVOLIO
Good morrow, cousin.
What sadness lengthens Romeo's hours?

ROMEO
Not having that which, having, makes them short.

BENVOLIO
In love?

ROMEO
Out—

BENVOLIO
Of love?

ROMEO
Out of her favour, where I am in love.
In sadness, cousin, I do love a woman.

BENVOLIO
I aim'd so near, when I supposed you loved.
Be ruled by me, forget to think of her.

ROMEO
O, teach me how I should forget to think.

BENVOLIO
By giving liberty unto thine eyes;
Examine other beauties.

Take thou some new infection to thy eye,
And the rank poison of the old will die.

SERVANT
God gi' good e'en; I pray, sir, can you read?

ROMEO
Ay, if I know the letters and the language.

SERVANT
Ye say honestly: rest you merry!

ROMEO
Stay, fellow; I can read.

(Reads.)

Mercutio and his brother Valentine; mine
uncle Capulet, his wife and daughters; my fair niece
Rosaline; Livia; Signior Valentio and his cousin
Tybalt. A fair assembly: whither should they come?

SERVANT
To our house. My master is the great rich Capulet; and if
you be not of the house of Montagues, I pray, come and
crush a cup of wine. Rest you merry!

(Exit.)

BENVOLIO
At this same ancient feast of Capulet's
Sups the fair Rosaline whom thou so loves,
With all the admired beauties of Verona:
Go thither, and with unattainted eye
Compare her face with some that I shall show,
And I will make thee think thy swan a crow.

ROMEO
    I'll go along, no such sight to be shown,
    But to rejoice in splendor of mine own.

(Exeunt.)

Act 1, Scene 3

A room in Capulet's house.

(Enter LADY CAPULET and Nurse.)

LADY CAPULET
    Nurse, where's my daughter? Call her forth to me.

NURSE
    What, lamb! What, ladybird!
    God forbid! Where's this girl? What, Juliet!

(Enter JULIET.)

JULIET
    How now, who calls?

NURSE
    Your mother.

JULIET
    Madam, I am here.
    What is your will?

LADY CAPULET
    This is the matter:
    Thou know'st my daughter's of a pretty age.

NURSE
    Faith, I can tell her age unto an hour.
    Thou wast the prettiest babe that e'er I nursed:
    And I might live to see thee married once,
    I have my wish.

LADY CAPULET
> Marry, that 'marry' is the very theme
> I came to talk of. Tell me, daughter Juliet,
> How stands your disposition to be married?

JULIET
> It is an honour that I dream not of.

NURSE
> An honour!

LADY CAPULET
> Well, think of marriage now:
> The valiant Paris seeks you for his love.

NURSE
> A man, young lady! Lady, such a man
> As all the world—why, he's a man of wax.

LADY CAPULET
> Verona's summer hath not such a flower.

NURSE
> Nay, he's a flower; in faith, a very flower.

LADY CAPULET
> What say you? Can you love the gentleman?
> This night you shall behold him at our feast;
> Speak briefly, can you like of Paris' love?

JULIET
> I'll look to like, if looking liking move.

(Enter a Servant.)

SERVANT
    Madam, the guests are come, supper served up, you
    called, my young lady asked for, the nurse cursed in
    the pantry, and everything in extremity. I beseech you,
    follow straight.

LADY CAPULET
    We follow thee.

(Exit Servant.)

    Juliet, the county stays.

NURSE
    Go, girl, seek happy nights to happy days.

(Exeunt.)

Act 1, Scene 4

A street.

(Enter ROMEO, MERCUTIO, and BENVOLIO.)

ROMEO
    Mercutio,
    Give me a torch: I am not for this ambling;
    Being but heavy, I will bear the light.

MERCUTIO
    Nay, gentle Romeo, we must have you dance.

ROMEO
    Not I, believe me: I have a soul of lead.

MERCUTIO
    You are a lover; borrow Cupid's wings,
    And soar with them above a common bound.

ROMEO
    Under love's heavy burden do I sink.
    I dreamt a dream tonight.

MERCUTIO
    And so did I.

ROMEO
    Well, what was yours?

MERCUTIO
    That dreamers often lie.

ROMEO
    In bed asleep, while they do dream things true.

MERCUTIO

O, then, I see Queen Mab hath been with you.
She is the fairies' midwife, and she comes
In shape no bigger than an agate stone
Drawn with a team of little atomies
Over men's noses as they lie asleep.
And in this state she gallops night by night
Through lovers' brains, and then they dream of love;
Which oft the angry Mab with blisters plagues,
Because their breaths with sweetmeats tainted are.

ROMEO

Peace, peace, Mercutio, peace!
Thou talk'st of nothing.

MERCUTIO

True, I talk of dreams,
Which are the children of an idle brain,
Which is as thin of substance as the air
And more inconstant than the wind—

BENVOLIO

This wind, you talk of, blows us from ourselves;
Supper is done, and we shall come too late.

ROMEO

I fear, too early: for my mind misgives
Some consequence yet hanging in the stars.

BENVOLIO
On, lusty gentlemen!

(Exeunt.)

Act 1, Scene 5

A hall in Capulet's house.

(Enter CAPULET, with JULIET and others of his house, meeting the Guests and Maskers.)

CAPULET
    Welcome, gentlemen! Ladies that have their toes
    Unplagued with corns will walk a bout with you.
    Ah ha, my mistresses! Which of you all
    Will now deny to dance? She that makes dainty,
    She, I'll swear, hath corns; am I come near ye now?

ROMEO
    (To a Serving man.)
    What lady's that which doth enrich the hand
    Of yonder knight?

SERVANT
    I know not, sir.

ROMEO
    O, she doth teach the torches to burn bright!
    Did my heart love till now? Forswear it, sight!
    For I ne'er saw true beauty till this night.

TYBALT
    This, by his voice, should be a Montague.
    Now, by the stock and honour of my kin,
    To strike him dead, I hold it not a sin.

CAPULET
    Why, how now, kinsman! Wherefore storm you so?

TYBALT

Uncle, this is a Montague, our foe.

CAPULET

Young Romeo is it?

TYBALT

'Tis he, that villain Romeo.

CAPULET

Content thee, gentle coz, let him alone;
Take no note of him; it is my will.

TYBALT

I'll not endure him.

CAPULET

He shall be endured:
What, goodman boy! I say, he shall, go to!

TYBALT

I will withdraw: but this intrusion shall
Now seeming sweet convert to bitt'rest gall.

(Exit.)

CAPULET

Come, musicians, play.
And quench the fire, the room is grown too hot.

(Music plays and they dance.)

ROMEO

(To JULIET.) If I profane with my unworthiest hand
This holy shrine, the gentle fine is this:

My lips, two blushing pilgrims, ready stand
To smooth that rough touch with a tender kiss.

JULIET
Good pilgrim, you do wrong your hand too much.
For saints have hands that pilgrims' hands do touch,
And palm to palm is holy palmers' kiss.

ROMEO
Have not saints lips, and holy palmers too?

JULIET
Ay, pilgrim, lips that they must use in prayer.

ROMEO
Then move not, while my prayer's effect I take.
Thus from my lips, by yours, my sin is purged.

JULIET
Then have my lips the sin that they have took.

ROMEO
Sin from thy lips? O trespass sweetly urged!
Give me my sin again.

JULIET
You kiss by the book.

NURSE
Madam, your mother craves a word with you.

ROMEO
What is her mother?

NURSE
Marry, bachelor,
Her mother is the lady of the house.

ROMEO
Is she a Capulet?
O dear account! My life is my foe's debt.

(Exeunt all but JULIET and Nurse.)

JULIET
Come hither, nurse. What is yond gentleman?

NURSE
His name is Romeo, and a Montague;
The only son of your great enemy.

JULIET
My only love sprung from my only hate!

NURSE
What's this? What's this?

JULIET
A rhyme I learn'd even now
Of one I danced withal.

(One calls within 'Juliet'.)

NURSE
Anon, anon!
Come, let's away; the strangers all are gone.

(Exeunt.)

Act 2, Scene 1

A lane by the wall of Capulet's orchard.

(Enter ROMEO.)

ROMEO
    Can I go forward when my heart is here?
    Turn back, dull earth, and find thy centre out.
    But soft, what light through yonder window breaks?
    It is the east, and Juliet is the sun.
    Arise, fair sun, and kill the envious moon.
    It is my lady, O, it is my love!
    O that she knew she were!

JULIET
    O Romeo, Romeo, wherefore art thou Romeo?
    Deny thy father and refuse thy name;
    Or, if thou wilt not, be but sworn my love,
    And I'll no longer be a Capulet.
    'Tis but thy name that is my enemy;
    Thou art thyself, though not a Montague.
    What's in a name? That which we call a rose
    By any other name would smell as sweet;
    So Romeo would, were he not Romeo call'd,
    Retain that dear perfection which he owes
    Without that title. Romeo, doff thy name,
    And for that name, which is no part of thee,
    Take all myself.

ROMEO
    I take thee at thy word:
    Call me but love, and I'll be new baptized;
    Henceforth I never will be Romeo.

JULIET
    Art thou not Romeo and a Montague?

ROMEO
    Neither, fair saint, if either thee dislike.

JULIET
    How cam'st thou hither, tell me, and wherefore?
    This place is death, considering who thou art,
    If any of my kinsmen find thee here.

ROMEO
    Alack, there lies more peril in thine eye
    Than twenty of their swords.

JULIET
    I would not for the world they saw thee here.
    Thou know'st the mask of night is on my face,
    Else would a maiden blush bepaint my cheek
    For that which thou hast heard me speak to-night.
    O gentle Romeo,
    If thou dost love, pronounce it faithfully:
    Or if thou think'st I am too quickly won,
    I'll frown and be perverse and say thee nay,
    So thou wilt woo; but else, not for the world.
    In truth, fair Montague, I am too fond,
    But trust me, gentleman, I'll prove more true
    Than those that have more cunning to be strange.

ROMEO
    Lady, by yonder blessed moon I vow—

JULIET
    O, swear not by the moon, the inconstant moon,
    Lest that thy love prove likewise variable.

ROMEO
    What shall I swear by?

JULIET

Well, do not swear: although I joy in thee,
I have no joy of this contract tonight:
It is too rash, too unadvised, too sudden;
Too like the lightning, which doth cease to be
Ere one can say 'It lightens.' Sweet, good night!

ROMEO

O, wilt thou leave me so unsatisfied?

JULIET

What satisfaction canst thou have tonight?

ROMEO

The exchange of thy love's faithful vow for mine.

JULIET

I gave thee mine before thou didst request it:
And yet I would it were to give again.

ROMEO

Wouldst thou withdraw it? For what purpose, love?

JULIET

But to be frank, and give it thee again.
And yet I wish but for the thing I have:
My bounty is as boundless as the sea,
My love as deep; the more I give to thee,
The more I have, for both are infinite.

(NURSE calls within.)

I hear some noise within;
Three words, dear Romeo, and good night indeed.
If that thy bent of love be honourable,
Thy purpose marriage, send me word tomorrow,

By one that I'll procure to come to thee,
Where and what time thou wilt perform the rite;
And all my fortunes at thy foot I'll lay
And follow thee my lord throughout the world.

NURSE
(*Within.*) Madam!

JULIET
I come, anon—But if thou mean'st not well,
I do beseech thee—

NURSE
(*Within.*) Madam!

JULIET
By and by, I come—
To cease thy suit, and leave me to my grief:
Tomorrow will I send.

ROMEO
So thrive my soul—

JULIET
Good night, good night! Parting is such sweet sorrow,
That I shall say good night till it be morrow.

(*Exit above.*)

ROMEO
Sleep dwell upon thine eyes, peace in thy breast!
Would I were sleep and peace, so sweet to rest!
Hence will I to my ghostly father's cell,
His help to crave, and my dear hap to tell.

(*Exit.*)

Act 2, Scene 2

Friar Laurence's cell.

(Enter FRIAR LAURENCE, with a basket.)

FRIAR LAURENCE
 Now, ere the sun advance his burning eye,
 The day to cheer and night's dank dew to dry,
 I must up-fill this osier cage of ours
 With baleful weeds and precious-juiced flowers.

(Enter ROMEO.)

ROMEO
 Good morrow, father.

FRIAR LAURENCE
 Benedicite!
 What early tongue so sweet saluteth me?
 Our Romeo hath not been in bed tonight?

ROMEO
 That is the truth; the sweeter rest was mine.

FRIAR LAURENCE
 God pardon sin! Wast thou with Rosaline?

ROMEO
 With Rosaline, my ghostly father? No;
 I have forgot that name, and that name's woe.

FRIAR LAURENCE
 That's my good son: but where hast thou been, then?

ROMEO

    I'll tell thee, ere thou ask it me again.
    I have been feasting with mine enemy,
    Where on a sudden one hath wounded me,
    That's by me wounded: both our remedies
    Within thy help and holy physic lies.

FRIAR LAURENCE

    Be plain, good son, and homely in thy drift;
    Riddling confession finds but riddling shrift.

ROMEO

    Then plainly know my heart's dear love is set
    On the fair daughter of rich Capulet:
    As mine on hers, so hers is set on mine;
    And all combined, save what thou must combine
    By holy marriage: when and where and how
    We met, we woo'd and made exchange of vow,
    I'll tell thee as we pass; but this I pray,
    That thou consent to marry us today.

FRIAR LAURENCE

    Holy Saint Francis, what a change is here!
    Is Rosaline, whom thou didst love so dear,
    So soon forsaken? Young men's love then lies
    Not truly in their hearts, but in their eyes.

ROMEO

    I pray thee, chide not.

FRIAR LAURENCE

    But come, young waverer, come, go with me,
    In one respect I'll thy assistant be;
    For this alliance may so happy prove,
    To turn your households' rancour to pure love.

ROMEO
    O, let us hence; I stand on sudden haste.

FRIAR LAURENCE
    Wisely and slow; they stumble that run fast.

(Exeunt.)

Act 2, Scene 3

A street.

(Enter BENVOLIO and MERCUTIO.)

MERCUTIO
Where the devil should this Romeo be?
Came he not home tonight?

BENVOLIO
Not to his father's; I spoke with his man.

MERCUTIO
Ah, that same pale hard-hearted wench, that Rosaline,
Torments him so, that he will sure run mad.

BENVOLIO
Tybalt, the kinsman of old Capulet,
Hath sent a letter to his father's house.

MERCUTIO
A challenge, on my life.

BENVOLIO
Romeo will answer it.

MERCUTIO
Alas poor Romeo! He is already dead; stabbed with a
white wench's black eye; and is he a man to encounter Tybalt?

BENVOLIO
Why, what is Tybalt?

MERCUTIO
O, he is the courageous captain of compliments!

(Enter ROMEO.)

Romeo, bonjour. You gave us the counterfeit fairly last night.

ROMEO
Pardon, good Mercutio, my business was great; and in such a case as mine a man may strain courtesy.

(Enter NURSE.)

MERCUTIO
A sail, a sail!

NURSE
God ye good morrow, gentlemen.

MERCUTIO
God ye good e'en, fair gentlewoman.

NURSE
Gentlemen, I desire some confidence with young Romeo.

BENVOLIO
She will indite him to some supper.

MERCUTIO
A bawd, a bawd, a bawd! So ho!

MERCUTIO
Romeo, will you come to your father's? We'll to dinner thither.

ROMEO
    I will follow you.

MERCUTIO
    Farewell, ancient lady. Farewell,

(Singing.)

    'lady, lady, lady.'

(Exeunt MERCUTIO and BENVOLIO.)

NURSE
    Marry, farewell! I pray you, sir, what saucy
    merchant was this?

ROMEO
    A gentleman, nurse, that loves to hear himself talk.

NURSE
    And he speak any thing against me, I'll take him
    down, scurvy knave! Pray you, sir, a word:
    my young lady bid me inquire you out.

ROMEO
    Nurse, commend me to thy lady and mistress. I
    protest unto thee—

NURSE
    Good heart, and, i' faith, I will tell her as much:
    Lord, Lord, she will be a joyful woman.

ROMEO
    What wilt thou tell her, nurse? Thou dost not mark me.

NURSE
　I will tell her, sir, that you do protest; which, as
　I take it, is a gentlemanlike offer.

ROMEO
　Bid her devise
　Some means to come to shrift this afternoon;
　And there she shall at Friar Laurence' cell
　Be shrived and married. Here is for thy pains.

NURSE
　No truly sir; not a penny.

ROMEO
　Go to; I say you shall.

NURSE
　This afternoon, sir? Well, she shall be there.

ROMEO
　Farewell. Commend me to thy lady.

NURSE
　Ay, a thousand times.

(Exeunt.)

Act 2, Scene 4

Capulet's orchard.

(Enter JULIET.)

JULIET
    The clock struck nine when I did send the nurse;
    In half an hour she promised to return.
    Now is the sun upon the highmost hill
    Of this day's journey, and from nine till twelve
    Is three long hours, yet she is not come.
    O God, she comes!

(Enter Nurse.)

    O honey nurse, what news?
    Now, good sweet nurse—O Lord, why look'st thou sad?

NURSE
    I am a-weary, give me leave awhile:
    Fie, how my bones ache!

JULIET
    I would thou hadst my bones, and I thy news:
    Nay, come, I pray thee, speak; good, good nurse, speak.

NURSE
    Jesu, what haste? Can you not stay awhile?
    Do you not see that I am out of breath?

JULIET
    How art thou out of breath, when thou hast breath
    To say to me that thou art out of breath?

NURSE

Well, you have made a simple choice; you know not
how to choose a man: Romeo! No, not he. Lord, how
my head aches!

JULIET

I' faith, I am sorry that thou art not well.
Sweet, sweet, sweet nurse, tell me, what says my love?

NURSE

Your love says, like an honest gentleman, and a
courteous, and a kind—where is your mother?

JULIET

Where is my mother! Why, she is within.
Where should she be? How oddly thou repliest!
'Your love says, like an honest gentleman,
Where is your mother?'

NURSE

O God's lady dear!
Are you so hot? Marry, come up, I trow;
Henceforward do your messages yourself.

JULIET

Come, what says Romeo?

NURSE

Have you got leave to go to shrift today?

JULIET

I have.

NURSE

Then hie you hence to Friar Laurence' cell;
There stays a husband to make you a wife.

Now comes the wanton blood up in your cheeks.
Hie you to church.
Go, I'll to dinner: hie you to the cell.

JULIET
Hie to high fortune! Honest nurse, farewell.

(Exeunt.)

Act 2, Scene 5

Friar Laurence's cell.

(Enter FRIAR LAURENCE and ROMEO.)

FRIAR LAURENCE
> So smile the heavens upon this holy act,
> That after hours with sorrow chide us not!

ROMEO
> Amen, amen! But come what sorrow can,
> It cannot countervail the exchange of joy
> That one short minute gives me in her sight:
> Do thou but close our hands with holy words,
> Then love-devouring death do what he dare;
> It is enough I may but call her mine.

FRIAR LAURENCE
> These violent delights have violent ends.
> Therefore love moderately; long love doth so;
> Too swift arrives as tardy as too slow.

(Enter JULIET.)

> Here comes the lady.

JULIET
> Good even to my ghostly confessor.

FRIAR LAURENCE
> Romeo shall thank thee, daughter, for us both.

JULIET
> As much to him, else is his thanks too much.

FRIAR LAURENCE
    Come, come with me, and we will make short work;
    For by your leaves, you shall not stay alone
    Till holy church incorporate two in one.

(Exeunt.)

Act 3, Scene 1

A *public place.*

(Enter MERCUTIO and BENVOLIO.)

BENVOLIO
    I pray thee, good Mercutio, let's retire:
    The day is hot, the Capulets abroad,
    And if we meet we shall not scape a brawl;
    For now, these hot days, is the mad blood stirring.

MERCUTIO
    Come, come, thou art as hot a Jack in thy mood as
    any in Italy.

BENVOLIO
    By my head, here comes a Capulet.

MERCUTIO
    By my heel, I care not.

(Enter TYBALT.)

TYBALT
    Gentlemen, good e'en: a word with one of you.

MERCUTIO
    And but one word with one of us? Couple it with
    something; make it a word and a blow.

TYBALT
    Mercutio, thou consort'st with Romeo—

MERCUTIO
    Consort! What, dost thou make us minstrels? Here's

my fiddlestick; here's that shall make you dance.
'Zounds, consort!

(Enter ROMEO.)

TYBALT
Well, peace be with you, sir: here comes my man.

MERCUTIO
But I'll be hanged, sir, if he wear your livery.

TYBALT
Romeo, the love I bear thee can afford
No better term than this: thou art a villain.

ROMEO
Tybalt, the reason that I have to love thee
Doth much excuse the appertaining rage
To such a greeting: villain am I none;
Therefore farewell; I see thou know'st me not.

TYBALT
Boy, this shall not excuse the injuries
That thou hast done me; therefore turn and draw.

ROMEO
I do protest, I never injured thee,
But love thee better than thou canst devise:
And so, good Capulet—which name I tender
As dearly as mine own—be satisfied.

MERCUTIO
O calm, dishonourable, vile submission!

(Draws.)

Tybalt, you rat-catcher, will you walk?

TYBALT
> What wouldst thou have with me?

MERCUTIO
> Good king of cats, nothing but one of your nine lives.

TYBALT
> I am for you.

(Drawing.)

ROMEO
> Gentle Mercutio, put thy rapier up.

MERCUTIO
> Come, sir, your passado.

(They fight.)

ROMEO
> Draw, Benvolio; beat down their weapons.
> Gentlemen, for shame, forbear this outrage!
> Tybalt, Mercutio, the prince expressly hath
> Forbidden bandying in Verona streets:
> Hold, Tybalt! Good Mercutio!

(TYBALT under ROMEO's arm stabs MERCUTIO, and flies with his followers.)

MERCUTIO
> I am hurt.
> A plague o' both your houses! I am sped.
> Is he gone, and hath nothing?

ROMEO
> Courage, man; the hurt cannot be much.

MERCUTIO
No, 'tis not so deep as a well, nor so wide as a
church-door; but 'tis enough, 'twill serve: ask for
me tomorrow, and you shall find me a grave man. Why
the devil came you between us? Help me into some house,
Benvolio.

(Exeunt MERCUTIO and BENVOLIO.)

ROMEO
This gentleman, the prince's near ally,
My very friend, hath got his mortal hurt
In my behalf; my reputation stain'd
With Tybalt's slander—Tybalt, that an hour
Hath been my kinsman!

(Re-enter BENVOLIO.)

BENVOLIO
O Romeo, Romeo, brave Mercutio's dead!

ROMEO
This day's black fate on more days doth depend;
This but begins the woe others must end.

(Re-enter TYBALT.)

Now, Tybalt, take the villain back again,
That late thou gav'st me; for Mercutio's soul
Is but a little way above our heads,
Staying for thine to keep him company.
Either thou, or I, or both must go with him.

TYBALT
Thou, wretched boy, that didst consort him here,
Shalt with him hence.

ROMEO
This shall determine that.

(They fight; TYBALT falls.)

BENVOLIO
Romeo, away, be gone!
The citizens are up, and Tybalt slain.
Stand not amazed: the prince will doom thee death,
If thou art taken: hence, be gone, away!

ROMEO
O, I am fortune's fool!

BENVOLIO
Why dost thou stay?

(Exit ROMEO.)
(Enter Citizens.)

FIRST CITIZEN
Which way ran he that kill'd Mercutio?
Tybalt, that murderer, which way ran he?

BENVOLIO
There lies that Tybalt.

FIRST CITIZEN
Up, sir, go with me;
I charge thee in the Prince's name, obey.

*(Enter Prince, attended; MONTAGUE, CAPULET, their
Wives, and others.)*

PRINCE
Benvolio, who began this bloody fray?

BENVOLIO
Tybalt, here slain, whom Romeo's hand did slay!
First Tybalt killed Mercutio, your kin.

LADY CAPULET
He is a kinsman to the Montague;
Affection makes him false; he speaks not true.
Romeo slew Tybalt, Romeo must not live.

PRINCE
Romeo slew him, he slew Mercutio;
Who now the price of his dear blood doth owe?

MONTAGUE
Not Romeo, Prince, he was Mercutio's friend;
His fault concludes but what the law should end,
The life of Tybalt.

PRINCE
And for that offence
Immediately we do exile him hence.
I have an interest in your heart's proceeding,
My blood for your rude brawls doth lie a-bleeding.
I will be deaf to pleading and excuses;
Nor tears nor prayers shall purchase out abuses:
Therefore use none. Let Romeo hence in haste,
Else, when he's found, that hour is his last.
Bear hence this body and attend our will:
Mercy but murders, pardoning those that kill.

(Exeunt.)

Act 3, Scene 2

Capulet's orchard.

(Enter JULIET.)

JULIET
    Gallop apace, you fiery-footed steeds,
    Towards Phoebus' lodging.
    Come, gentle night, come, loving, black-brow'd night,
    Give me my Romeo, and when he shall die,
    Take him and cut him out in little stars,
    And he will make the face of heaven so fine
    That all the world will be in love with night
    And pay no worship to the garish sun.

(Enter Nurse.)

    Now, nurse, what news?

NURSE
    Ah, well-a-day! He's dead, he's dead, he's dead!
    We are undone, lady, we are undone!

JULIET
    Can heaven be so envious?

NURSE
    Romeo can,
    Though heaven cannot: O Romeo, Romeo!

JULIET
    What devil art thou, that dost torment me thus?
    Hath Romeo slain himself?

NURSE

I saw the wound, I saw it with mine eyes—

JULIET

O, break, my heart! Break at once!

NURSE

O Tybalt, Tybalt, the best friend I had!
That ever I should live to see thee dead!

JULIET

What storm is this that blows so contrary?
Is Romeo slaughter'd, and is Tybalt dead?
My dear-loved cousin, and my dearer lord?

NURSE

Tybalt is gone, and Romeo banished;
Romeo that kill'd him, he is banished.

JULIET

O God! Did Romeo's hand shed Tybalt's blood?

NURSE

It did, it did; alas the day, it did!

JULIET

O serpent heart, hid with a flowering face!
O that deceit should dwell
In such a gorgeous palace!

NURSE

There's no trust,
No faith, no honesty in men; all perjured.
Shame come to Romeo!

JULIET

Blister'd be thy tongue
For such a wish!

NURSE

Will you speak well of him that kill'd your cousin?

JULIET

Shall I speak ill of him that is my husband?
But wherefore, villain, didst thou kill my cousin?
Some word there was, worser than Tybalt's death,
That murder'd me: I would forget it fain;
'Tybalt is dead, and Romeo—banished.'
That 'banished,' that one word 'banished,'
Hath slain ten thousand Tybalts. Tybalt's death
Was woe enough, if it had ended there.
But with a rearward following Tybalt's death,
'Romeo is banished,' to speak that word,
Is father, mother, Tybalt, Romeo, Juliet,
All slain, all dead. 'Romeo is banished!'

NURSE

Hie to your chamber: I'll find Romeo
To comfort you: I wot well where he is.
Hark ye, your Romeo will be here at night:
I'll to him; he is hid at Laurence' cell.

JULIET

O, find him! Give this ring to my true knight,
And bid him come to take his last farewell.

(Exeunt.)

Act 3, Scene 3

Friar Laurence's cell.

(Enter FRIAR LAURENCE and ROMEO.)

ROMEO
　　Father, what news? What is the prince's doom?

FRIAR LAURENCE
　　A gentler judgment vanish'd from his lips:
　　Not body's death, but body's banishment.

ROMEO
　　Ha, banishment! Be merciful, say 'death';
　　There is no world without Verona walls,
　　But purgatory, torture, hell itself.

FRIAR LAURENCE
　　O deadly sin! O rude unthankfulness!
　　This is dear mercy, and thou seest it not.

ROMEO
　　'Tis torture, and not mercy: heaven is here,
　　Where Juliet lives; and every cat and dog
　　Live here in heaven and may look on her,
　　But Romeo may not, he is banished.
　　O friar, the damned use that word in hell;
　　Howlings attend it. How hast thou the heart
　　To mangle me with that word 'banished'?

FRIAR LAURENCE
　　Thou fond mad man, hear me but speak a word.

ROMEO
　　Thou canst not speak of that thou dost not feel:

Wert thou as young as I, Juliet thy love,
An hour but married, Tybalt murdered,
Doting like me and like me banished,
Then mightst thou speak, then mightst thou tear thy hair,
And fall upon the ground, as I do now.

(Sound within.)

FRIAR LAURENCE
Who's there? Whence come you? What's your will?

(Enter Nurse.)

NURSE
I come from Lady Juliet.

FRIAR LAURENCE
Welcome, then.

NURSE
O, he is even in my mistress' case.

ROMEO
Spak'st thou of Juliet? How is it with her?
Doth she not think me an old murderer?

NURSE
O, she says nothing, sir, but weeps and weeps,
And Tybalt calls, and then on Romeo cries,
And then down falls again.

ROMEO
As if that name
Did murder her; as that name's cursed hand
Murder'd her kinsman. O, tell me, friar, tell me,
In what vile part of this anatomy

Doth my name lodge? Tell me, that I may sack
The hateful mansion.

(Drawing his sword.)

FRIAR LAURENCE
What, rouse thee, man! Thy Juliet is alive.
Go, get thee to thy love, as was decreed,
Ascend her chamber, hence and comfort her.
But look thou stay not till the watch be set,
For then thou canst not pass to Mantua,
Where thou shalt live, till we can find a time
To blaze your marriage, reconcile your friends,
Beg pardon of the prince, and call thee back.
Go before, nurse; commend me to thy lady,
And bid her hasten all the house to bed,
Which heavy sorrow makes them apt unto:
Romeo is coming.

NURSE
Here, sir, a ring she bid me give you, sir.
Hie you, make haste, for it grows very late.

(Exit.)

ROMEO
How well my comfort is revived by this!

FRIAR LAURENCE
Go hence, good night; and here stands all your state:
Either be gone before the watch be set,
Or by the break of day disguised from hence.
Sojourn in Mantua.'Tis late: farewell; good night.

ROMEO
Farewell.

(Exeunt.)

Act 3, Scene 4

A room in Capulet's house.

(Enter CAPULET, LADY CAPULET, and PARIS.)

CAPULET
    Things have fall'n out, sir, so unluckily
    That we have had no time to move our daughter.
    Look you, she loved her kinsman Tybalt dearly.
    Sir Paris, I will make a desperate tender
    Of my child's love: I think she will be ruled
    In all respects by me; nay, more, I doubt it not.
    Acquaint her, wife, of my son Paris' love;
    And bid her, mark you me, on Wednesday next—
    But, soft—what day is this?

PARIS
    Monday, my lord.

CAPULET
    Monday! Ha, ha! Well, Wednesday is too soon,
    O' Thursday let it be: o' Thursday, tell her,
    She shall be married to this noble earl.
    What say you to Thursday?

PARIS
    My lord, I would that Thursday were tomorrow.

CAPULET
    Well, get you gone: o' Thursday be it, then.
    Prepare her, wife, against this wedding-day.
    Farewell, my lord.
    Good night.

(Exeunt.)

Act 3, Scene 5

Juliet's chamber.

(Enter ROMEO and JULIET.)

JULIET
   Wilt thou be gone? It is not yet near day:
   It was the nightingale, and not the lark,
   That pierced the fearful hollow of thine ear.

ROMEO
   It was the lark, the herald of the morn,
   No nightingale. Look, love, what envious streaks
   Do lace the severing clouds in yonder east.
   I must be gone and live, or stay and die.

JULIET
   Yond light is not daylight, I know it, I:
   It is some meteor that the sun exhales
   To be to thee this night a torchbearer,
   And light thee on thy way to Mantua.
   Therefore stay yet; thou need'st not to be gone.

ROMEO
   Let me be ta'en, let me be put to death.
   I have more care to stay than will to go.
   Come, death, and welcome! Juliet wills it so.
   How is't, my soul? Let's talk; it is not day.

JULIET
   It is, it is: hie hence, be gone, away!
   It is the lark that sings so out of tune.
   O, now be gone; more light and light it grows.

ROMEO
More light and light; more dark and dark our woes!

(Enter Nurse, to the chamber.)

NURSE
Madam!

JULIET
Nurse?

NURSE
Your lady mother is coming to your chamber:
The day is broke; be wary, look about.

(Exit.)

JULIET
Then, Romeo, let day in, and let life out.

ROMEO
Farewell, farewell! One kiss, and I shall leave.

JULIET
O think'st thou we shall ever meet again?

ROMEO
I doubt it not; and all these woes shall serve
For sweet discourses in our time to come.

JULIET
O God, I have an ill-divining soul!

ROMEO
Trust me, love. Adieu, adieu!

(Exit.)

LADY CAPULET
    (Within.) Ho, daughter, are you up?

JULIET
    Who is't that calls?

(Enter LADY CAPULET.)

LADY CAPULET
    Why, how now, Juliet?
    Evermore weeping for your cousin's death?
    And if thou couldst, thou couldst not make him live.
    Therefore have done;
    For now I'll tell thee joyful tidings, girl.

JULIET
    And joy comes well in such a needy time.

LADY CAPULET
    Marry, my child, early next Thursday morn,
    The County Paris, at Saint Peter's Church,
    Shall happily make thee there a joyful bride.

JULIET
    Now, by Saint Peter's Church and Peter too,
    He shall not make me there a joyful bride.
    I pray you, tell my lord and father, madam,
    I will not marry yet; and, when I do, I swear
    It shall be Romeo, whom you know I hate,
    Rather than Paris. These are news indeed!

LADY CAPULET
    Here comes your father; tell him so yourself,
    And see how he will take it at your hands.

(Enter CAPULET and Nurse.)

CAPULET
> How now, a conduit, girl? What, still in tears?
> Have you deliver'd to her our decree?

LADY CAPULET
> Ay, sir; but she will none, she gives you thanks.
> I would the fool were married to her grave!

CAPULET
> Is she not proud? Doth she not give us thanks?
> That we have wrought so worthy a gentleman to be her groom?

JULIET
> Not proud, you have; but thankful, that you have.
> Proud can I never be of what I hate.
> But thankful even for hate that is meant love.

CAPULET
> Thank me no thankings, nor proud me no prouds,
> But fettle your fine joints 'gainst Thursday next,
> To go with Paris to Saint Peter's Church,
> Or I will drag thee on a hurdle thither.
> Out, you green-sickness carrion! Out, you baggage!

LADY CAPULET
> Fie, fie! What, are you mad?

JULIET
> Good father, I beseech you on my knees—

CAPULET
> Hang thee, young baggage! Disobedient wretch!
> I tell thee what: get thee to church o' Thursday,
> Or never after look me in the face!

NURSE
    God in heaven bless her!

CAPULET
    Peace, you mumbling fool!

LADY CAPULET
    You are too hot.

CAPULET
    Thursday is near; lay hand on heart, advise:
    And you be mine, I'll give you to my friend;
    And you be not, hang, beg, starve, die in the streets!
    For, by my soul, I'll ne'er acknowledge thee.
    Trust to't, bethink you; I'll not be forsworn.

(Exit.)

JULIET
    O, sweet my mother, cast me not away!
    Delay this marriage for a month, a week;
    Or, if you do not, make the bridal bed
    In that dim monument where Tybalt lies.

LADY CAPULET
    Talk not to me, for I'll not speak a word.
    Do as thou wilt, for I have done with thee.

(Exit.)

JULIET
    O God!—O nurse, how shall this be prevented?
    Some comfort, nurse.

NURSE
Faith, here it is.
Romeo is banish'd; and all the world to nothing.
Then, since the case so stands as now it doth,
I think it best you married with the county.
O, he's a lovely gentleman!
Romeo's a dishclout to him. Beshrew my very heart,
I think you are happy in this second match,
For it excels your first.

JULIET
Speak'st thou from thy heart?

NURSE
And from my soul too.

JULIET
Amen!

NURSE
What?

JULIET
Well, thou hast comforted me marvellous much.
Go in, and tell my lady I am gone,
Having displeased my father, to Laurence' cell,
To make confession and to be absolved.

NURSE
Marry, I will; and this is wisely done.

(Exit.)

JULIET
    O most wicked fiend! Go, counsellor;
    Thou and my bosom henceforth shall be twain.
    I'll to the friar, to know his remedy:
    If all else fail, myself have power to die.

(Exit.)

Act 4, Scene 1

Friar Laurence's cell.

(Enter FRIAR LAURENCE and PARIS.)

FRIAR LAURENCE
   On Thursday, sir? The time is very short.

PARIS
   My father Capulet will have it so;
   And I am nothing slow to slack his haste.

FRIAR LAURENCE
   You say you do not know the lady's mind:
   Uneven is the course, I like it not.

PARIS
   Immoderately she weeps for Tybalt's death,
   And therefore have I little talk'd of love.
   Now, sir, her father counts it dangerous
   That she doth give her sorrow so much sway,
   And in his wisdom hastes our marriage,
   To stop the inundation of her tears.

FRIAR LAURENCE
   Look, sir, here comes the lady towards my cell.

(Enter JULIET.)

PARIS
   Happily met, my lady and my wife!

JULIET
   That may be, sir, when I may be a wife.

PARIS

That may be must be, love, on Thursday next.

JULIET

What must be shall be.

FRIAR LAURENCE

That's a certain text.

PARIS

Come you to make confession to this father?

JULIET

To answer that, I should confess to you.

PARIS

Poor soul, thy face is much abused with tears.

JULIET

Are you at leisure, holy father, now;
Or shall I come to you at evening mass?

FRIAR LAURENCE

My leisure serves me, pensive daughter, now.
My lord, we must entreat the time alone.

PARIS

God shield I should disturb devotion!
Juliet, on Thursday early will I rouse ye:
Till then adieu, and keep this holy kiss.

(Exit.)

JULIET

Come weep with me; past hope, past cure, past help!

FRIAR LAURENCE

    Ah, Juliet, I already know thy grief;
    It strains me past the compass of my wits:
    I hear thou must, and nothing may prorogue it,
    On Thursday next be married to this county.

JULIET

    Tell me not, friar, that thou hear'st of this,
    Unless thou tell me how I may prevent it.
    Give me some present counsel, or, behold,
    'Twixt my extremes and me this bloody knife
    Shall play the umpire.

FRIAR LAURENCE

    Hold, daughter: I do spy a kind of hope.
    If, rather than to marry County Paris,
    Thou hast the strength of will to slay thyself,
    Then is it likely thou wilt undertake
    A thing like death to chide away this shame.

JULIET

    O, bid me leap, rather than marry Paris,
    From off the battlements of any tower.

FRIAR LAURENCE

    Hold, then; go home, be merry, give consent
    To marry Paris. Wednesday is tomorrow.
    Tomorrow night look that thou lie alone.
    Take thou this vial, being then in bed,
    And this distilled liquor drink thou off;
    When presently through all thy veins shall run
    A cold and drowsy humour, for no pulse
    Shall keep his native progress, but surcease.
    No warmth, no breath, shall testify thou liv'st;
    The roses in thy lips and cheeks shall fade
    Like death, when he shuts up the day of life;

Each part shall, stiff and stark, appear like death.
Thou shalt continue two and forty hours,
And then awake as from a pleasant sleep.
Now, when the bridegroom in the morning comes
To rouse thee from thy bed, there art thou dead.
Thou shalt be borne to that same ancient vault
Where all the kindred of the Capulets lie.
In the meantime, against thou shalt awake,
Shall Romeo by my letters know our drift,
And hither shall he come: and he and I
Will watch thy waking, and that very night
Shall Romeo bear thee hence to Mantua.

JULIET
Give me, give me!

FRIAR LAURENCE
Hold, get you gone. Be strong and prosperous
In this resolve. I'll send a friar with speed
To Mantua, with my letters to thy lord.

JULIET
Love give me strength, and strength shall help afford.
Farewell, dear father!

(Exeunt.)

Act 4, Scene 2

Hall in Capulet's house.

(Enter CAPULET, LADY CAPULET, Nurse.)

CAPULET
>What, is my daughter gone to Friar Laurence?

NURSE
>Ay, forsooth.

CAPULET
>Well, he may chance to do some good on her:
>A peevish self-will'd harlotry it is.

NURSE
>See where she comes from shrift with merry look.

(Enter JULIET.)

CAPULET
>How now, my headstrong! Where have you been gadding?

JULIET
>Where I have learn'd me to repent the sin
>Of disobedient opposition
>To you and your behests, and am enjoin'd
>By holy Laurence to fall prostrate here,
>And beg your pardon. Pardon, I beseech you!
>Henceforward I am ever ruled by you.

CAPULET
>Send for the county; go tell him of this:
>I'll have this knot knit up tomorrow morning.

JULIET
    Nurse, will you go with me into my closet,
    To help me sort such needful ornaments
    As you think fit to furnish me tomorrow?

LADY CAPULET
    No, not till Thursday; there is time enough.

CAPULET
    Go, nurse, go with her: we'll to church tomorrow.

(Exeunt JULIET and Nurse.)

LADY CAPULET
    We shall be short in our provision:
    'Tis now near night.

CAPULET
    Tush, I will stir about,
    And all things shall be well, I warrant thee, wife.
    Go thou to Juliet, help to deck up her.
    I'll not to bed tonight; let me alone;
    I'll play the housewife for this once. What, ho!
    They are all forth. Well, I will walk myself
    To County Paris, to prepare him up
    Against tomorrow. My heart is wondrous light,
    Since this same wayward girl is so reclaim'd.

(Exeunt.)

Act 4, Scene 3

Juliet's chamber.

(Enter JULIET and Nurse.)

JULIET
    But, gentle nurse, I pray thee, leave me to myself tonight.

(Enter LADY CAPULET.)

LADY CAPULET
    What, are you busy, ho? Need you my help?

JULIET
    No, madam; we have cull'd such necessaries
    As are behoveful for our state tomorrow.
    So please you, let me now be left alone,
    And let the nurse this night sit up with you;
    For I am sure you have your hands full all,
    In this so sudden business.

LADY CAPULET
    Good night:
    Get thee to bed, and rest; for thou hast need.

(Exeunt LADY CAPULET and Nurse.)

JULIET
    Farewell! God knows when we shall meet again.
    I have a faint cold fear thrills through my veins.
    Come, vial.
    What if this mixture do not work at all?
    Shall I be married then tomorrow morning?
    No, no: this shall forbid it. Lie thou there.

(Laying down her dagger.)

How if, when I am laid into the tomb,
I wake before the time that Romeo
Come to redeem me? There's a fearful point!
Shall I not then be stifled in the vault,
To whose foul mouth no healthsome air breathes in,
And there die strangled ere my Romeo comes?
Romeo, Romeo, Romeo! Here's drink—I drink to thee.

(She falls upon her bed, within the curtains.)

Act 4, Scene 4

Hall in Capulet's house.

(Enter CAPULET.)

CAPULET
    Come, stir, stir, stir! The second cock hath crow'd!
    Look to the baked meats, spare not for the cost.
    Good faith, 'tis day: the county is here!
    Nurse! What, ho! What, nurse, I say!

(Enter Nurse.)

    Go waken Juliet, go and trim her up;
    I'll go and chat with Paris: hie, make haste,
    Make haste; the bridegroom he is come already:
    Make haste, I say.

(Exeunt.)

Act 4, Scene 5

Juliet's chamber.

(Enter Nurse.)

NURSE
Mistress, what, mistress! Juliet! Fast, I warrant her, she:
Why, love, I say, madam! What, not a word?
I must needs wake you. Lady! lady! lady!
Alas, alas! Help, help! My lady's dead!
O, weraday, that ever I was born!
Some aqua vitae, ho! My lord, my lady!

(Enter LADY CAPULET.)

LADY CAPULET
What noise is here?

NURSE
O lamentable day!

LADY CAPULET
What is the matter?

NURSE
Look, look! O heavy day!

LADY CAPULET
O me, O me! My child, my only life,
Revive, look up, or I will die with thee!
Help, help! Call help.

(Enter CAPULET.)

CAPULET
> For shame, bring Juliet forth; her lord is come.

NURSE
> She's dead, deceased, she's dead; alack the day!

LADY CAPULET
> Alack the day, she's dead, she's dead, she's dead!

CAPULET
> Hah, let me see her: out, alas, she's cold:
> Her blood is settled, and her joints are stiff;
> Life and these lips have long been separated.

NURSE
> O lamentable day!

LADY CAPULET
> O woeful time!

(Enter FRIAR LAURENCE and PARIS.)

FRIAR LAURENCE
> Come, is the bride ready to go to church?

CAPULET
> Ready to go, but never to return.
> O son, the night before thy wedding-day
> Hath Death lain with thy wife. There she lies.

PARIS
> Have I thought long to see this morning's face,
> And doth it give me such a sight as this?

LADY CAPULET
Accursed, unhappy, wretched, hateful day!
Most miserable hour that e'er time saw!

NURSE
O woe! O woeful, woeful, woeful day!

PARIS
Beguiled, divorced, wronged, spited, slain!
Most detestable death, by thee beguil'd!

CAPULET
O child, O child, my soul, and not my child!

FRIAR LAURENCE
Peace, ho, for shame! Confusion's cure lives not
In these confusions. Heaven and yourself
Had part in this fair maid; now heaven hath all,
And all the better is it for the maid.
Dry up your tears, and stick your rosemary
On this fair corse; and as the custom is,
In all her best array bear her to church.

CAPULET
All things that we ordained festival,
Turn from their office to black funeral.

FRIAR LAURENCE
Sir, go you in, and, madam, go with him;
And go, Sir Paris. Everyone prepare
To follow this fair corse unto her grave.
The heavens do lour upon you for some ill;
Move them no more by crossing their high will.

(Exeunt.)

Act 5, Scene 1

Mantua. A street.

(Enter ROMEO.)

ROMEO
　　If I may trust the flattering truth of sleep,
　　My dreams presage some joyful news at hand:
　　I dreamt my lady came and found me dead—
　　And breathed such life with kisses in my lips,
　　That I revived, and was an emperor.

(Enter BALTHASAR.)

　　News from Verona!—How now, Balthasar?
　　Dost thou not bring me letters from the friar?
　　How doth my lady?
　　For nothing can be ill, if she be well.

BALTHASAR
　　Then she is well, and nothing can be ill.
　　Her body sleeps in Capel's monument,
　　And her immortal part with angels lives.
　　I saw her laid low in her kindred's vault,
　　And presently took post to tell it you:
　　O, pardon me for bringing these ill news.

ROMEO
　　Is it even so? Then I defy you, stars!
　　Thou know'st my lodging: get me ink and paper,
　　And hire post-horses; I will hence tonight.

BALTHASAR
　　I do beseech you, sir, have patience:

Your looks are pale and wild, and do import
Some misadventure.

ROMEO
    Tush, thou art deceived:
    Leave me, and do the thing I bid thee do.
    Hast thou no letters to me from the friar?

BALTHASAR
    No, my good lord.

ROMEO
    No matter: get thee gone,
    And hire those horses; I'll be with thee straight.

(Exit BALTHASAR.)

    Well, Juliet, I will lie with thee tonight.
    Let's see for means:
    I do remember an apothecary—
    And hereabouts he dwells—meagre were his looks,
    Sharp misery had worn him to the bones.
    Noting this penury, to myself I said
    'And if a man did need a poison now,
    Here lives a caitiff wretch would sell it him.'
    O, this same thought did but forerun my need;
    And this same needy one must sell it me.
    What, ho, apothecary!

(Enter Apothecary.)

APOTHECARY
    Who calls so loud?

ROMEO
    Come hither, now. I see that thou art poor:

Hold, there is forty ducats: let me have
A dram of poison, such soon-speeding gear
As will disperse itself through all the veins
That the life-weary taker may fall dead.

APOTHECARY
Such mortal drugs I have; but Mantua's law
Is death to any he that utters them.

ROMEO
The world affords no law to make thee rich;
Then be not poor, but break it, and take this.

APOTHECARY
My poverty, but not my will, consents.

ROMEO
I pay thy poverty, and not thy will.

APOTHECARY
Put this in any liquid thing you will,
And drink it off; and, if you had the strength
Of twenty men, it would dispatch you straight.

ROMEO
There is thy gold, worse poison to men's souls,
Than these poor compounds that thou mayst not sell.
I sell thee poison; thou hast sold me none.
Farewell: buy food, and get thyself in flesh.
Come, cordial and not poison, go with me
To Juliet's grave; for there must I use thee.

(Exeunt.)

Act 5, Scene 2

A churchyard; in it a tomb belonging to the Capulets.

(Enter PARIS.)

PARIS
    Sweet flower, with flowers thy bridal bed I strew.
    The obsequies that I for thee will keep
    Nightly shall be to strew thy grave and weep.

(Noise within.)

    What cursed foot wanders this way tonight,
    To cross my obsequies and true love's rite?
    Muffle me, night, awhile.

(Retires.)
(Enter ROMEO and BALTHASAR.)

    Hold, take this letter; early in the morning
    See thou deliver it to my lord and father.
    Whate'er thou hear'st or seest, stand all aloof,
    And do not interrupt me in my course.

BALTHASAR
    I will be gone, sir, and not trouble you.

ROMEO
    So shalt thou show me friendship. Take thou that:
    Live and be prosperous, and farewell, good fellow.

BALTHASAR
    (Aside.) For all this same, I'll hide me hereabout:
    His looks I fear, and his intents I doubt.

(Retires.)

ROMEO
(Opens the tomb.)
O my love, my wife,
Death that hath suck'd the honey of thy breath
Hath had no power yet upon thy beauty.

PARIS
(Comes forward.)
Stop thy unhallow'd toil, vile Montague!
Condemned villain, I do apprehend thee:
Obey, and go with me; for thou must die.

ROMEO
I must indeed; and therefore came I hither.
Good gentle youth, tempt not a desperate man.
Fly hence, and leave me: think upon these gone;
Let them affright thee. I beseech thee, youth,
Put not another sin upon my head
By urging me to fury: O, be gone!
By heaven, I love thee better than myself;
For I come hither arm'd against myself.
Stay not, be gone; live, and hereafter say
A madman's mercy bid thee run away.

PARIS
I do defy thy conjuration,
And apprehend thee for a felon here.

ROMEO
Wilt thou provoke me? Then have at thee, boy!

(They fight.)

PARIS
O, I am slain!

(Dies.)

ROMEO
Mercutio's kinsman, noble County Paris!
What said my man? I think
He told me Paris should have married Juliet.
Ah, dear Juliet,
Why art thou yet so fair? Eyes, look your last!
Arms, take your last embrace, and lips, O you
The doors of breath, seal with a righteous kiss
A dateless bargain to engrossing death!
Come, bitter conduct, come, unsavoury guide!
Here's to my love!

(Drinks.)

O true apothecary!
Thy drugs are quick. Thus with a kiss I die.

(Dies.)
(Enter, at the other end of the churchyard, FRIAR LAURENCE.)

FRIAR LAURENCE
Saint Francis be my speed! Fear comes upon me.
Romeo ne'er received the letter I did send.

(Enters the tomb.)

Romeo! O, pale! Who else? What, Paris too?
Ah, what an unkind hour
Is guilty of this lamentable chance!

(JULIET wakes.)

JULIET
    O comfortable friar! Where is my lord?
    I do remember well where I should be,
    And there I am. Where is my Romeo?

(Noise within.)

FRIAR LAURENCE
    I hear some noise. Lady, come from that nest
    Of death, contagion, and unnatural sleep.
    A greater power than we can contradict
    Hath thwarted our intents. Come, come away.
    Thy husband in thy bosom there lies dead;
    And Paris too. Come, I'll dispose of thee
    Among a sisterhood of holy nuns.
    Stay not to question, for the watch is coming;
    Come, go, good Juliet.

(Noise again.)

    I dare no longer stay.

JULIET
    Go, get thee hence, for I will not away.

(Exit FRIAR LAURENCE.)

    What's here? A cup closed in my true love's hand?
    Poison, I see, hath been his timeless end.
    O churl, drunk all, and left no friendly drop
    To help me after? I will kiss thy lips;
    Haply some poison yet doth hang on them.

(Kisses him.)

FIRST WATCHMAN
(*Within.*) This way, this is the place.

JULIET
Yea, noise? Then I'll be brief. O happy dagger!

(*Snatching ROMEO's dagger.*)

This is thy sheath.

(*Stabs herself.*)
(*Falls on ROMEO's body and dies.*)
(*Enter Watch.*)

FIRST WATCHMAN
Search about the churchyard:
Go, some of you, whoe'er you find attach.
Pitiful sight! Here lies the county slain,
And Juliet bleeding, warm, and newly dead,
Who here hath lain these two days buried.
Go, tell the Prince: run to the Capulets:
Raise up the Montagues.

(*Re-enter some of the Watch, with BALTHASAR.*)

SECOND WATCHMAN
Here's Romeo's man; we found him in the churchyard.

FIRST WATCHMAN
Hold him in safety, till the Prince come hither.

(*Re-enter others of the Watch, with FRIAR LAURENCE.*)

THIRD WATCHMAN
Here is a friar, that trembles, sighs and weeps,
As he was coming from this churchyard side.

FIRST WATCHMAN
    A great suspicion: stay the friar too.

(Enter the PRINCE and Attendants.)

PRINCE
    What misadventure is so early up,
    That calls our person from our morning's rest?

(Enter CAPULET, LADY CAPULET, and others.)

CAPULET
    What should it be, that they so shriek abroad?

LADY CAPULET
    The people in the street cry Romeo,
    Some Juliet, and some Paris; and all run
    With open outcry toward our monument.

PRINCE
    What fear is this which startles in our ears?

FIRST WATCHMAN
    Sovereign, here lies the County Paris slain;
    And Romeo dead; and Juliet, dead before,
    Warm and new kill'd.

(Enter MONTAGUE and others.)

PRINCE
    Come, Montague; for thou art early up,
    To see thy son and heir more early down.

MONTAGUE
    Alas, my liege, my wife is dead tonight.
    Grief of my son's exile hath stopp'd her breath.
    What further woe conspires against mine age?

PRINCE

    Look, and thou shalt see.

    Bring forth the parties of suspicion.

    Friar, say at once what thou dost know in this.

FRIAR LAURENCE

    Romeo, there dead, was husband to that Juliet;

    And she, there dead, that Romeo's faithful wife.

    I married them, and their stol'n marriage day

    Was Tybalt's doomsday, whose untimely death

    Banish'd the new-made bridegroom from the city,

    For whom, and not for Tybalt, Juliet pined.

    You, to remove that siege of grief from her,

    Betroth'd and would have married her perforce

    To County Paris. Then comes she to me,

    And, with wild looks, bid me devise some mean

    To rid her from this second marriage.

    Then gave I her, so tutor'd by my art,

    A sleeping potion, which so took effect

    As I intended, for it wrought on her

    The form of death. Meantime I writ to Romeo,

    That he should hither come as this dire night,

    To help to take her from her borrow'd grave,

    Being the time the potion's force should cease.

    But he which bore my letter, Friar John,

    Was stay'd by accident, and yesternight

    Return'd my letter back. Then all alone

    At the prefixed hour of her waking,

    Came I to take her from her kindred's vault;

    Meaning to keep her closely at my cell,

    Till I conveniently could send to Romeo.

    But when I came, some minute ere the time

    Of her awaking, here untimely lay

    The noble Paris and true Romeo dead.

    She wakes; and I entreated her come forth

    And bear this work of heaven with patience.

But then a noise did scare me from the tomb;
And she, too desperate, would not go with me,
But, as it seems, did violence on herself.
If aught in this
Miscarried by my fault, let my old life
Be sacrificed, some hour before his time,
Unto the rigour of severest law.

PRINCE

We still have known thee for a holy man.
Where's Romeo's man? What can he say in this?

BALTHASAR

I brought my master news of Juliet's death;
And then in post he came from Mantua.
This letter he early bid me give his father.

PRINCE

The letter doth make good the friar's words,
Their course of love, the tidings of her death:
And here he writes that he did buy a poison
Of a poor 'pothecary, and therewithal
Came to this vault to die, and lie with Juliet.
Where be these enemies? Capulet! Montague!
See what a scourge is laid upon your hate,
That heaven finds means to kill your joys with love.
And I for winking at your discords too
Have lost a brace of kinsmen: all are punish'd.

CAPULET

O brother Montague, give me thy hand.
This is my daughter's jointure, for no more
Can I demand.

MONTAGUE

But I can give thee more:

For I will raise her statue in pure gold,
That while Verona by that name is known,
There shall no figure at such rate be set
As that of true and faithful Juliet.

CAPULET
As rich shall Romeo's by his lady's lie;
Poor sacrifices of our enmity!

PRINCE
A glooming peace this morning with it brings;
The sun, for sorrow, will not show his head.
Go hence, to have more talk of these sad things.
Some shall be pardon'd, and some punished:
For never was a story of more woe
Than this of Juliet and her Romeo.

(Exeunt.)